uʏ̊ s,

THAT SHOULD NEVER HAVE HAPPENED!

I KNOW YOU WERE FIRED, BUT WOULD YOU MIND
TAKING THE MAIL WITH YOU ON THE WAY DOWN ?

ACCORDING TO THE CERTIFICATE IT'S A 100 YEAR OLD
TEXAS PINE . . . I GUESS HE MUST BE A CATTLE THIEF.

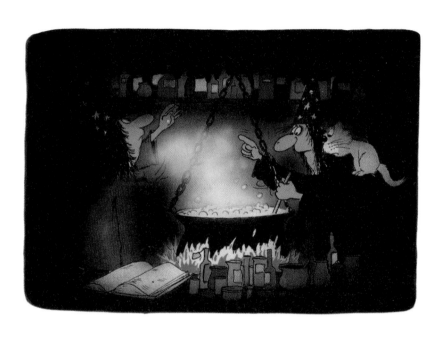

THE KETCHUP IS ON THE LEFT, BETWEEN
THE SPIDER LEGS AND THE TOAD EGGS.

IT'S MY INVENTION, IT PLAYS "I LOST MY HEAD OVER YOU."

MY HUSBAND'S VERY ILL.
CAN I RETURN THE TIE IF HE DIES BEFORE CHRISTMAS?

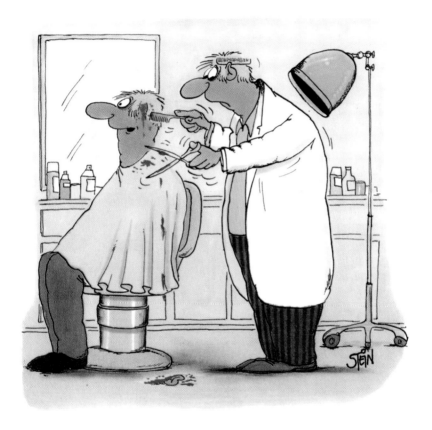

NO PROBLEM. JUST PUT IT IN A DOGGY BAG.

YOU RANG SIRE ?

ALRIGHT I'M IN

THREE QUEENS !

THREE KINGS !

I HAVE NO IDEA . . . HE WAS ALREADY HERE WHEN WE ARRIVED.

GLAD YOU'RE BOTH HERE! COULD ONE OF YOU TRY TO GET THE
CHAINSAW FROM HIM WHILE THE OTHER IDENTIFIES THE BABYSITTER?

PERSONALLY I THINK FRED SHOULD TRY A DIFFERENT SUNTAN LOTION.

IN THE KING'S NAME, I DECLARE THE NEW GUILLOTINE OPEN . . .

HE SWALLOWED A MAGNET !

TRY IT – MAYBE **YOU** CAN TALK HIM INTO GIVING US HIS ROLEX . . .

I HAVE TO FEED HIM MORNING NOON AND NIGHT . . .
I CAN'T WAIT TILL HE GROWS UP AND STARTS ATTACKING PEOPLE.

OFFICALLY YOU ARE NOT ALLOWED TO TAKE DOGS INTO CHINA
BUT YOU COULD DECLARE HIM AS A SNACK . . .